# A baking fairytale

# Flossie

## CRUMS

## and the Fairy Cupcake Ball

## Helen Nathan

### Illustrations by Catherine Black. Artwork by Kevin Shaw

First published in September 2009 by B. Dutton Publishing Limited, Alfred House, Hones Business Park, Farnham, Surrey, GU9 8BB.

Copyright: Helen Nathan, Catherine Black and Kevin Shaw 2009

ISBN-13: 978-1-905113-13-2

Publisher: Beverley Dutton

Editor: Jenny Stewart

Art Director/Designer: Sarah Richardson

Sub Editor: Jenny Royle

Graphic Designer: Zena Manicom

Publishing Assistant: Louise Pepé

Cake Designer: Helen Nathan

Cake Stylist: Ann Skipp

Photography: Alister Thorpe

Printed in Slovenia

*To Molly, Rosie and Lottie – you make each day magical.*

H.N.

*To my beloved Gideon and India, without whom I would never have discovered the importance of cupcakes or coloured pencils.*

C.B.

## Acknowledgements

Thank you to Beverley and the team at B. Dutton Publishing. To Larry, Christopher, Biffy and Rotha.

##  A note for cake makers

Some of the ingredients in this book are available from specialist cake decorating suppliers. Wherever you see the cupcake symbol, please refer to the stockist information at the back of this book for special items to make your cakes look magical. A useful conversion chart is also given on page 55.

Have you ever wondered how fairy cakes got their name? I used to wonder as well, until one day, I found out...

### A note for fairy fans

See if you can find a fairy on every page – sometimes you might have to look really hard to find them. Grown-ups will often miss them, so you might have to help.

By the way, I'm Flossie. I am ninety-two days away from my eighth birthday, which means I am seven and three quarters. I love cooking but I hate clearing up, I love dressing up but I hate getting dressed in the morning, and best of all I love cooking in my dressing up clothes.

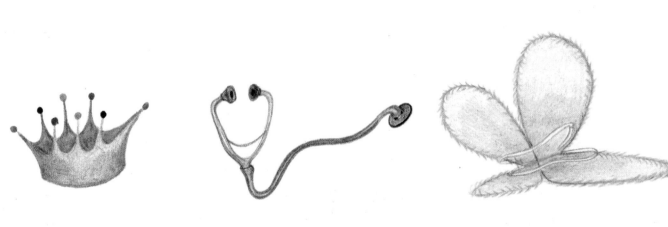

Every house has fairies. I love them, though sometimes they can be very annoying when they sit on my head.

Grown-ups hardly ever see them but that's because they don't concentrate properly.

Our fairies live in the chestnut tree outside the kitchen window. They call it the kingdom of Romolonia.

7

I first met the fairies last summer. It happened when mum and I were having a pretend fairy picnic.

We collected acorn hats for wine glasses. For plates we used shells we'd found on the beach on holiday.

Mum and I made our favourite chocolate cake and cut it into small slices (the right size for fairies, of course). This is the best chocolate cake ever. I have to let you in on a secret: when people taste this cake they think I must have had cookery lessons because it is so delicious. Even my six-year-old brother Billie can make it, it's that easy.

# Flossie's very impressive, especially tasty
## Chocolate Cake

## Ingredients

175g sugar

175g softened butter

200g drinking chocolate

75g self-raising flour

4 eggs

Mini marshmallows

## Method

1  Ask a grown-up to turn the oven to 190°C and grease a 20cm (8") heart-shaped cake tin.

2  Put all the ingredients into a mixing bowl and mix them together until everything is really chocolaty.

3  Scrape the mixture into the cake tin and bake the cake for 40 minutes. It might still be a bit wobbly in the middle when it comes out but trust me, that's a good thing.

4  Only when it is completely cold, gently tip the cake onto a plate and decorate with mini marshmallows.

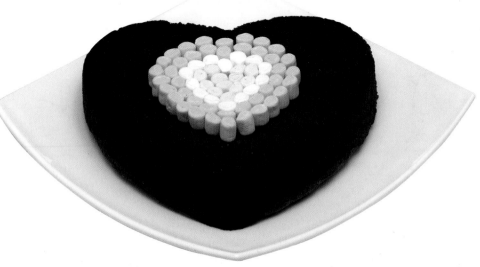

As well as the cake, I made little sausage rolls that looked like fairy pillows, sandwiches shaped like stars and heart-shaped biscuits with red and pink icing.

I wanted to see the fairies but mum said they wouldn't visit until I'd gone to bed.

I asked if I could sleep under the stars that night and wait for them, but she said that I should sleep in my own bed as my snoring might frighten them away. She says my snoring is almost as loud as dad's but that's ridiculous as the walls wobble when he sleeps and I'm sure I would wake myself up if I snored that loudly.

The next morning I woke up really early. I crept outside and the grass was still a bit wet and soggy. I couldn't believe my eyes: there were six fairies sitting in a circle. When they saw me they whispered to each other and then shyly came and introduced themselves.

"Hello, I'm Coco," said the tallest fairy in a rich, soft voice. She had the coolest ringlets, like little springs in her dark hair. "These are my friends from Romolonia," she continued, and beckoned the other fairies closer.

The next fairy fluttered forward, shimmering and sparkling. "My name is Crystal," she said as she shook my hand.

A fairy called Caramel curtsied as she introduced herself. She seemed shy but her radiant smile and brightly coloured dress warmed up the chilly morning air.

The fourth fairy bowed and nodded her head. "Hello Flossie, I'm called Cherry and I've been watching you grow up. I've seen you play under my cherry tree. I'm so glad we can be friends."

There were two more fairies to meet. The smallest fairy flitted up to me – she smelt of warm sunshine. "Hello, I'm a Honey fairy but my friends call me Bee. It's so nice to meet you, but you're very big."

I giggled and Coco introduced me to Minty, who laughed as well and shook my hand. I loved her at once as she was a bit scruffy, just like me!

17

Even so, I was really glad I'd brushed my hair and was wearing my best pyjamas.

"We usually hide from humans but your cake was so delicious we just need to have a quick chat with you," explained Coco. She told me that they had been discussing Queen Rosie's birthday celebrations, which take place every year on midsummer's eve.

"We're the catering team and are planning the menu for the party. Queen Rosie has been miserable for weeks."

"She shouts at us to tidy up the tree and complains when we drop our wings on the floor at bedtime," explained Cherry. "Without a happy queen, Romolonia is dreadful place to be."

"You are our last hope," sighed Minty. "We are stuck for new ideas, you see. She wants delicious cakes and we haven't got any new recipes."

"She's so grumpy she forgot to kiss me this morning," sniffed Honey.

"I think I can help!" I said excitedly.

"Mum and I love to cook and we are always creating new cakes to bake. Our chocolate, banana and spaghetti cake wasn't great but the strawberry light as a feather cake was delicious.

The fairies giggled, then went into a little huddle and started whispering.

Suddenly, Coco flew behind the tree, dragged out a long, stripy wand and gave it to me. "Sprinkle just a shake of magic glitter from the wand over the cakes just before you finish and they will become magic fairy cakes fit for a fairy queen," she said.

"You mustn't tell anyone you have seen us," whispered Caramel, but I explained that if they wanted mum's help I would have to tell her – I'm not allowed to open the oven by myself and mum also doesn't like me keeping secrets from her.

"We just have to make a quick call to the spiders to check that it would be OK. They are in charge of security," said Crystal. (I guess that's why they are called spy-ders.)

As she reached for her tiny pink phone, Rocket, our border collie dashed down the garden to see me.

"Ahhh, a furry earth creature! Let's go!" squealed the fairies and flitted off.

When I realised that they had vanished, I rushed indoors
to tell mum.

"We need to make black forest basket cakes for Cherry...
I can't believe she's known me since I was a baby. Don't you think
we should make some peppermint cream and chocolate cakes for
Minty? You know, she loves football mum, just like me! Hmm, and
we'll need something really special for Queen Rosie."

Mum looked up from her magazine but then carried on
eating her breakfast. She didn't believe a word I was saying,
even when I told her that we were the fairies' last hope of
making Queen Rosie smile and we had to make cakes for
the fairy ball. I think secretly she was pleased that the six
fairies from the catering team had loved our chocolate cake,
but she still wouldn't take what I was saying seriously.

You would think that grown-ups would understand really important
things like that, but sometimes they just don't get anything.

I sulked back to the chestnut tree and plopped
myself down on the grass.

23

Just then I heard a bird chirping, but not up in a branch; where my hand was resting. I spread open my fingers and saw Crystal's tiny pink mobile phone, which was covered in fairy dust. The ring tone was the blackbird's song and there were no numbers, just tiny stars on the keypad.

By the time I realised what it was, the fairy phone had stopped ringing, so I picked it up and ran indoors.

You should have seen mum's face when I showed it to her! We were both still staring at the phone in amazement when suddenly it rang again. Crystal magically appeared looking flustered and a bit bothered. "Oh, there it is," she declared, then picked up the phone, nodded at mum and disappeared again.

Mum watched Crystal fly out of the window then turned to me with a surprised expression on her face. For once, she couldn't think of anything to say!

That afternoon we put our aprons on and baked the best cakes we had ever made.

The first cake I wanted to make was for Minty.
(Don't tell the others, but I think I like her best.)

I hoped Minty would love them as much as I do!

# Double Chocolate Chip Cupcakes
## with Chocolate and Peppermint Cream Icing

## Ingredients

### Cakes

115g softened butter

115g caster sugar

85g self-raising flour

30g cocoa powder

2 eggs

1/2 teaspoon vanilla extract

50g chocolate chips

### Icing

🧁 Ready-to-roll chocolate icing

🧁 Ready-to-roll white icing

1/4 teaspoon peppermint essence

### Finishing touch

🧁 12 mini mint humbugs

🧁 Edible fairy glitter

### Makes about 12 cupcakes

## Method

1. Ask a grown-up to turn on the oven to 190°C.

2. Put all the ingredients into a mixing bowl and mix them all up for a few minutes. You don't want any lumpy bits of butter.

3. Put 12 cupcake paper cases into a 12-hole fairy cake tin and spoon the mixture evenly between the cases.

4. Bake the cakes for 15 minutes.

5. Ask a grown-up to take them out of the oven and place them carefully onto a wire rack to cool.

6. When the cakes are cool, sprinkle a little bit of icing sugar on a clean work surface such as the kitchen table. Blend the peppermint essence into the white icing by kneading it with your hands and then use a rolling pin to roll out the icing. Roll out the chocolate icing as well. (The icing sugar stops the icing sticking.)

7. Using lots of different round cutters make brown and minty circles. (Ready-to-roll icing is just like play dough but you get to eat it – how cool is that!) Pile the circles on top of each other and put a mint humbug on the top. (You can use edible glue to stick it in place if you need to.)

8. Sprinkle with edible fairy glitter to make the cakes magical!

I made my own tiny weeny sweets for Caramel by unwrapping
large ones and getting mum to cut them into fairy portions. I
invented my own toffee icing too!

# Vanilla and Toffee Cupcakes

## Ingredients

### Cakes
115g softened butter
115g caster sugar
115g self-raising flour
2 eggs
½ teaspoon vanilla extract

### Icing
50g softened butter
4 tablespoons caramel toffee
(dulce de leche)
400g icing sugar
2 dessertspoons cold water

### Finishing touch
Toffee, fudge or chocolate-coated caramel pieces popped inside multi-coloured wrappers
Edible fairy glitter

Makes about 12 cupcakes

## Method

1. Ask a grown-up to turn the oven to 190°C.

2. Mix all the cake ingredients together really well in a mixing bowl. When the ingredients are well mixed, place 12 cupcake cases into a 12-hole cupcake tin and spoon the mixture into the cases.

3. Bake in the oven for 15 minutes then ask a grown-up to take them out and place them onto a wire rack to cool.

4. To make the icing, mix the icing sugar with the other ingredients until the mixture has a gooey, shiny consistency. Once the cakes are cool, pipe the icing in a big swirl, or spread lots of icing onto each cake using the back of a teaspoon. A good tip is to dip the spoon into warm water first – this makes the icing more spreadable.

5. To finish off the cakes, pile up small pieces of toffee, fudge or caramel in the centre of each cake.

6. Sprinkle with edible fairy glitter to make the cakes magical!

So many cakes, so little time to decide what would make the queen smile most. After making Caramel's cakes, I decided to make a cupcake basket for my kind and gentle friend, Cherry. I hoped Queen Rosie would like it too – I didn't want her to be grumpy on her birthday. (Maybe she was going to be 30 – mum said that's enough to make anyone miserable.)

# Black Forest Cupcake Basket
## with Whipped Cream and Fresh Cherries

## Ingredients

### Cakes

115g softened butter

115g caster sugar

85g self-raising flour

30g cocoa powder

2 eggs

½ teaspoon vanilla extract

### Icing

Small pot of double cream, whipped

### Finishing touch

Fresh cherries

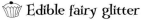 Edible fairy glitter

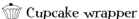 Cupcake wrapper

### Makes about 12 cupcakes

## Method

1. Ask a grown-up to turn the oven to 190°C.

2. Using a wooden spoon and a mixing bowl, mix all the cake ingredients together really well. If you feel that your arm is about to drop off, you could get help and use an electric whisk.

3. Put 12 cupcake paper cases into a 12-hole fairy cake tin and spoon the mixture evenly between the cases.

4. Bake in the oven for 15 minutes. When baked, ask a grown-up to take them out of the oven and allow to cool on a wire rack.

5. When cool, put the cream on and stick cherries all over. Mmmmmm!

6. Place each cake in a cupcake wrapper 'basket'. I made these baskets while the cupcakes were in the oven by sticking a strip of paper to a cupcake wrapper to make a handle.

7. Sprinkle edible fairy glitter over the cherries to make the cakes magical!

Crystal had beautiful,
long, blonde hair.
I think she's an ice
fairy – I wonder if
she likes skating?

Anyway, I love coconut ice so this cake seemed like a good idea. I
put a crystal 'wand' in the top so that if she lost anything again she
could 'magic' it back to Romolonia. Mum was muttering something
about dizzy blondes but I had no idea what she was on about.

# Coconut Cupcakes

## with Maple Syrup Frosting and a Sugar Crystal Wand

### Ingredients

#### Cakes

115g softened butter
115g caster sugar
115g self-raising flour
2 eggs
25g desiccated coconut

#### Icing

50g melted butter
4 tablespoons maple syrup
400g icing sugar
2 dessertspoons cold water
A saucer filled with desiccated coconut

#### Finishing touch

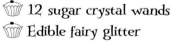 12 sugar crystal wands
Edible fairy glitter

### Makes about 12 cupcakes

### Method

1 Ask a grown-up to turn on the oven to 190°C.

2 Using a wooden spoon, mix all the ingredients for the cake together really well in a mixing bowl.

3 Arrange 12 cupcake cases in a cupcake tin and spoon the mixture into the cases.

4 Bake in the oven for 15 minutes, then ask a grown-up to take them out of the oven and place them on a wire rack to cool.

5 When the cakes are cool, make the icing by mixing all the ingredients except the coconut together. (Mum and I use an electric whisk to save time.)

6 Spread on the icing or pipe it on using a piping bag then roll the top of the cakes in the coconut. Lastly, sprinkle with edible fairy glitter, stick a 'wand' in the top and make a wish!

33

I knew Bee the Honey fairy would smile her
dimply smile when she saw these!

(I think these cakes should
be called 'BEELICIOUS!')

# Honey Cupcakes
## with Vanilla Icing, Honeycomb Bars and Bees

## Ingredients

### Cakes

115g softened butter

115g caster sugar

115g self-raising flour

2 eggs

1 tablespoon honey

### Icing

50g melted butter

400g icing sugar

3 tablespoons cold water

2 teaspoons vanilla essence

### Finishing touch

4 honeycomb chocolate bars

🧁 A packet of sugar bees really makes the cake special

🧁 Edible fairy glitter

Makes about 12 cupcakes

## Method

1. When you're ready to start, ask a grown-up to turn on the oven to 190°C.

2. Mix all the ingredients together really well in a bowl.

3. Put 12 cupcake paper cases into a 12-hole fairy cake tin and spoon the mixture evenly between the cases.

4. Bake for 15 minutes.

5. Ask a grown-up to take the cakes out of the oven and place them onto a wire rack to cool.

6. Wait until the cakes are cool, then whisk the ingredients for the icing together and spread onto the cakes.

7. Build up a pile of cut up honeycomb chocolate bars and decorate with sugar bees. You can use a little icing or edible glue to hold the bees in place.

8. Sprinkle with edible fairy glitter to make the cakes magical!

Coco was definitely 'in charge' so I needed to impress her with this recipe!

The raspberry icing is delicious; the only difficult part is not licking it all out of the bowl before it goes on the cupcakes. Mum made the swirls the first time to show me how to do them, but once you get the hang of it, you can do them yourself - you just need to press down quite hard on the wheel.

# White Chocolate Cupcakes
## with Fresh Raspberry Icing and Cocoa Swirls

## Ingredients

### Cakes
125g softened butter
100g white chocolate
200g caster sugar
125g milk
1 egg, lightly whisked
190g self-raising flour
1 teaspoon vanilla essence

### Icing
🧁 1 packet of fresh raspberry fondant icing

### Finishing touch
🧁 1 Swiss chocolate roulette
🧁 Edible fairy glitter

Makes about 12 cupcakes

## Method

1 Ask a grown-up to turn on the oven to 180°C, then ask them to melt the first four ingredients in a saucepan.

2 Allow the mixture to cool for ten minutes, then mix this and the other cake ingredients together in a big bowl.

3 Spoon the cake mixture into 12 cupcake cakes, place these into a fairy cake baking tray and bake for 20 minutes.

4 Ask a grown-up to take the cakes out of the oven and put them on a wire rack. While they are cooling, add water to the fondant icing following the instructions on the side of the packet. When the icing is lovely and smooth, spoon it onto the cupcakes.

5 To make the chocolate swirls, push down on the chocolate roulette using the handle of the chocolate swirl machine and turn it in a circle. If you don't have one of these machines in the kitchen, you could use chocolate flakes instead.

6 Sprinkle with edible fairy glitter to make the cakes magical!

I knew I wanted to make rose cupcakes for Queen Rosie and I needed to collect petals to scatter round them.

The day before, granny had been in the garden with her scissors and collected all the petals she could find. She makes these beautiful little bags and fills them with roses and lavender, then sews them up and puts them in our knicker drawers.

I didn't think roses from granny's knickers would be suitable for a queen so I climbed into the bushes at the bottom of the garden and found one plant granny had overlooked.

(The truth is, she probably had seen it, but it was a bit of a tight squeeze to get to and granny does like cakes, if you know what I mean.)

This cake had to be the very best cake I had ever made in the whole wide world. I was keeping my fingers, toes and eyes crossed that she would like it.

# Queen Rosie's Royal Rose Cupcakes
## with Sugar Diamonds

## Ingredients

### Cakes

115g sugar
115g softened butter
115g self-raising flour
2 eggs
½ teaspoon rose essence

### Icing

25g melted butter
400g icing sugar
4 tablespoons cold water
1 drop of natural pink food colouring

### Finishing touch

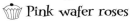 Pink wafer roses
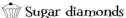 Sugar diamonds
🧁 Edible fairy glitter
🧁 Cupcake wrapper

Makes about 12 cupcakes

## Method

1　Ask a grown-up to turn on the oven to 190°C.

2　Mix all the cake ingredients together really well.

3　Put 12 cupcake paper cases into a 12-hole fairy cake tin and spoon the mixture evenly between the cases.

4　Bake for 15 minutes and then ask a grown-up to place them carefully onto a wire rack to cool.

5　When cool, place all of the icing ingredients into a mixing bowl and whisk them together for a few minutes. You might need some help with this.

6　If you are feeling very creative and you can find a piping bag, you can fill this up with icing and swirl it onto the cake (it looks SO impressive). Just remember to push the icing right down the bag and hold the top tightly shut, otherwise all the icing will squeeze onto the table, not the cake! Alternatively, spread it on with a teaspoon (there's a special tip for this on page 29).

7　Here's the best bit of all – put the roses and diamonds on the cake and sprinkle with edible fairy glitter just before serving. Place the cake into a cupcake wrapper if you have one then look at the cake sparkle!

"They look wonderful!" exclaimed Coco, who had flown in through the open window and was flitting above my head. Mum pretended not to look surprised to see fairies again but she was definitely astonished because her jaw dropped down and her eyebrows shot up. I think she was still getting used to the idea that fairies really do exist.

"I'm so glad you like them," I said happily.

"We were wondering whether you would like to come and present the cakes to the queen yourself," said Coco, then added, "I'm afraid your mum's too big to come."

Mum still looked a bit funny but nodded and said, "Off you go then sweetheart, as long as you don't go any further than the garden." I looked at her gratefully as I put on my shoes as quickly as I could. Mum hurriedly put all the cakes onto a tray and gave them to me before I followed Coco to the chestnut tree.

WELCOME
please leave your
wands at the door

44

As were got nearer, the bark on the tree ripped and a door creaked open. There was a tiny doormat saying 'Welcome, please leave your wands at the door.' Coco took the wand she'd lent me and tapped my head with it. In a squillionth of a second I was as small as her and heading through the tree to Romolonia!

The ball had already started and there was so much to see I didn't know what to look at first.

The ballroom was enormous but the floor was covered in grass and daisies. There were four large apple trees, one in each corner of the room, laden down with golden apples that twinkled and sparkled. Hundreds of swings hung from the ceiling and were intertwined with gold thread and flowers. The silver tables had bowls of grapes in every colour you can imagine.

Beautiful fairies were everywhere, all licking multicoloured lollies that went pop and made and the whole room smell of peppermint. Minty, Honey, Caramel, Cherry and Crystal flew over to greet me and I felt a little bit less nervous.

Seated on a tall throne in the centre of the room was Queen Rosie. Her dress was made from rose petals and dewdrops and she had a crown of intertwined roses perched on her hair.

She looked so beautiful and I still had flour on my t-shirt. It wouldn't usually worry me as I'm not too fussy about that sort of thing, but it's not every day you get to meet the Queen of Romolonia.

I curtsied very carefully, making sure I didn't drop all the cakes. She beckoned me forward and stared at the goodies in front of her.

I was really worried that she wouldn't like them, but the next thing she did was smile a wonderful wide smile and ask if by any chance the rose cake was her birthday present from me?

"Yes, your majesty. I hope you like it, mum and I spent ages getting everything ready for this special occasion."

She nodded and Minty flew to my side, hugged me then tugged me away.

 "Wow, did you see that smile? We haven't seen the queen that happy in Romolonia for more than a month. I don't know how to thank you, Flossie."

Before I could object Cherry took my hand and whispered that it was sadly time to go. Then she showed me the way back to our kitchen.

It felt like I had been away for ages but mum said it had only been a few minutes. I couldn't believe it! I felt so tired from all the excitement so I laid down on my bed for just a moment and fell asleep instantly.

That night I dreamt of all the wonderful things I had seen in Romolonia.

The next morning there was a bumpy package under my pillow with a note. It was from Queen Rosie and was written in gold on fabric as thin as tissue paper, I think it was made from silk. At the top, the words 'Royal Warrant' were printed in ornate lettering. It read:

# Royal Warrant

## Dear Flossie,

It is with immense pleasure that I write to congratulate you and your mother on producing the finest fairy cupcakes I have ever tasted.

I grant you the Romolonian special seal of approval for cake making and I request that you make these recipes available to everyone.

As a reward for all your hard work, I would like to give you a glitter wand from all of the fairies here in Romolonia.

Yours faithfully

## Rosie
Queen of the Fairies

P.S. Please ensure the glitter wand is used carefully as it is full of magic.

Even now I'm almost eight and nearly a grown-up,
I still remember how happy I felt that morning
– it's not every day you are granted a royal warrant,
given a magic wand, or handed an opportunity to
make the queen of the fairies smile again.

You should have seen the look on my brother Billie's
face when I showed him my gift from Queen Rosie.
He's desperate for a wand as well, but boys can't
always be trusted with magical things. Goodness
knows what he would get up to if I ever let
him into Romolonia!

## Here are a few helpful baking tips that I wanted to share with you...

1. Wash your hands when you are baking – fairies don't like germs.

2. Mum says it's healthier to cook with natural ingredients because they're better for you.

3. She also says if you can, walk to the shops with a grown up for the ingredients rather than drive as you'll enjoy the cake more because of the exercise. (Does flying with fairies count as exercise?)

4. It's a good idea to wear an apron so you don't get too mucky. (Can't see the point myself but mum wanted me to write that down.)

5. Always ask a grown-up to put things in and take things out of the oven for you.

6. Licking the spoon and bowl is yummy, but it is dangerous if you have used raw eggs. If you smile sweetly, you might be allowed to lick the icing bowl after you have finished decorating your fairy cakes.

7. If you enjoy cooking, always help to tidy up. For some reason my mum gets really cross if I just run off and play before everything is clean and tidy. (Washing up is quite fun really.)

# Conversions

## Dry Measurements

| METRIC | IMPERIAL |
|--------|----------|
| 15g | ½oz |
| 30g | 1oz |
| 60g | 2oz |
| 90g | 3oz |
| 125g | 4oz (¼lb) |
| 155g | 5oz |
| 185g | 6oz |
| 220g | 7oz |
| 250g | 8oz (½lb) |
| 280g | 9oz |
| 315g | 10oz |
| 345g | 11oz |
| 375g | 12oz (¾lb) |
| 410g | 13oz |
| 440g | 14oz |
| 470g | 15oz |
| 500g | 16oz (1lb) |
| 750g | 24oz (1½lb) |
| 1kg | 32oz (2lb) |

## Liquid Measurements

| METRIC | IMPERIAL | US CUPS |
|--------|----------|---------|
| 30ml | 1fl oz | ⅛ cup |
| 60ml | 2fl oz | ¼ cup |
| 90ml | 3fl oz | ⅜ cup |
| 120ml | 4fl oz | ½ cup |
| 140ml | 5fl oz | ⅔ cup |
| 170ml | 6fl oz | ¾ cup |
| 200ml | 7fl oz | ⅞ cup |
| 230ml | 8fl oz | 1 cup |
| 260ml | 9fl oz | 1⅛ cups |
| 290ml | 10fl oz | 1¼ cups |
| 500ml | 17½fl oz | 2 cups |
| 600ml | 120fl oz | 2½ cups |
| 1 litre | 1¾ pints | 4 cups |

To find out more about Flossie Crums and her family, enjoy other great recipes and purchase any of the special baking items mentioned in this book, please visit www.flossiecrums.com or www.squires-shop.com

Squires Kitchen
Squires House
3 Waverley Lane
Farnham
Surrey
GU9 8BB
UK

0845 22 55 67 1/2
www.squires-shop.com